The Wonderful Picnic

Story by
Hilary Faith Jones

Illustration by
Honor Ayres

By the same author:
Awakenings
Waiting for Jesus
Awakenings (spoken word cassette)

Published by
The Leprosy Mission International
2002

Distributed by TLM Trading Limited,
The Leprosy Mission's trading company.
PO Box 212
Peterborough
PE2 5GD
Phone: 01733 239252
Fax: 01733 239258
Email: enquires@tlmtrading.com

Editorial and design by Craft Plus Publishing Ltd
53 Crown Street, Brentwood, Essex CM14 4BD

Printed and bound in Spain by Bookprint, S.L. - Barcelona
A catalogue record for this book is available from the British Library.
ISBN 0 902731 47 5

This book belongs to...

I wonder if there is a ladybird on each page...

Foreword

Like many young children, my son Ryan already has an inquiring and receptive mind and I firmly believe in the importance of teaching him Christian values and beliefs at an early age.

The Bible is full of wonderful stories with great relevance to our everyday lives but the challenge lies in simplifying them and making them appeal to the imagination of a small child.

In *The Wonderful Picnic*, Hilary Faith Jones meets that challenge perfectly. The story is amusingly told and the illustrations are a delight – Ryan particularly loves the purple donkey! Minimus and his friends take us along with them to meet up with Jesus in the most natural way. We all hope our own children 'meet' Jesus as a friend too.

I am sure that this book will be a welcome addition to any child's library and will be read time and time again. Whether you buy it to read to your toddler or as a gift for older children who will read it for themselves, I cannot recommend *The Wonderful Picnic* too highly.

Katrina

Hello!

I'm Minimus the mouse.

I live with a carpenter. One day he left his shop full of wood and set off on a **long** journey.

I wasn't going to be left behind so
I crept into his bag.

Now I go everywhere with him.
He's my best friend!

Lots of people come along with us.
I don’t mind, but the problem with grown-ups is that they talk so much. Sometimes I can’t get a squeak in edgeways.

I’m glad my carpenter friend is good at listening!

And guess what?
I've made lots of
new friends too...

This is Bumble the donkey.
He's ever so soft and gentle.

He lets me ride on his back.
I like giving Bumble hugs.

And this is Esmé the bird.

She tells me what it's like to fly through the air and feel the wind in her feathers.

Esmé can sing like an angel.
I've never seen an angel but I think
they must be very beautiful.

And this is Seraphina the cat.
When she walks,
she lifts her paws
very high, pretending
to be posh.

But I don't think she's very clever. Cats are supposed to eat mice and Seraphina never hurts me.

She even lets me play with her tail.

And this is my friend Scruffy the puppy.
He's not posh at all!

He’s so funny he makes us all laugh, even the grown-ups!

That's my carpenter friend
over there.
His name is Jesus.

He's brilliant at telling stories!

No wonder hundreds of people
want to listen to him.

We like listening too but they've been talking and talking for ages!

I do hope Jesus hasn't forgotten about tea. We're ever so hungry.

Wibbly-wobbly
whiskers!
I heard someone
mention food!

Oh-oh. I knew it.
No one's brought
any food with them.
Dizzy-aster!

Hello little boy!
Have you got something for Jesus?

Looks a bit squishy squashy to me.

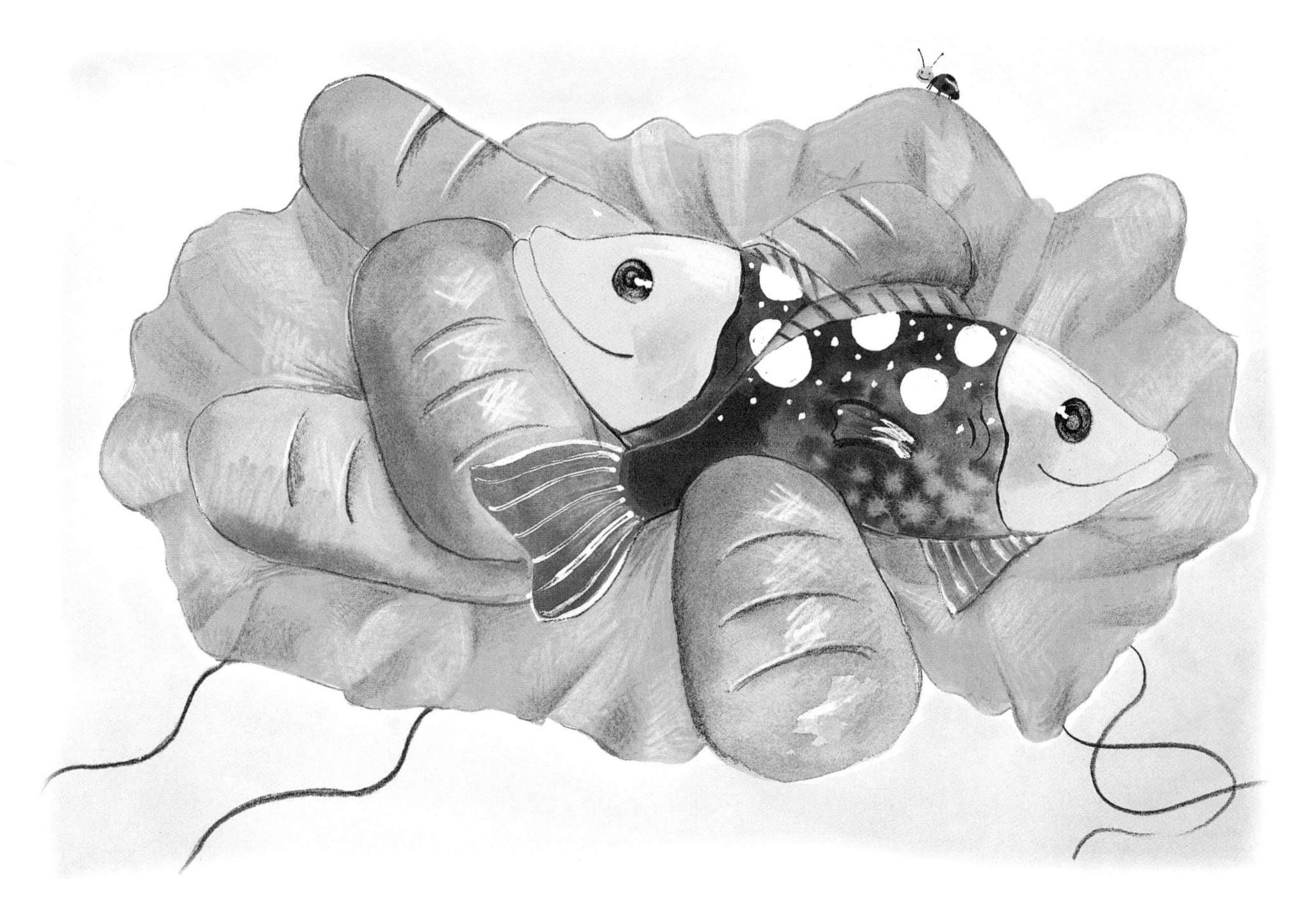

Only five loaves and two fishes.
That won't be enough for everyone to eat. Oh dear!

Look! Jesus is saying thank you to God for the food.

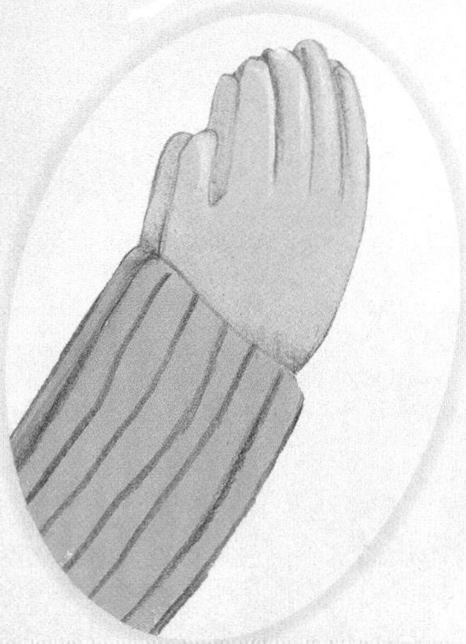

Scruffy, we
had better
close our eyes
and say thank
you like Jesus.

WOW-WHEE!!
Look at the great big picnic
Jesus has made!

Everyone has enough
to eat **and** he hasn't
forgotten us!
Thanks Jesus!

Yummy in my tummy. That feels better!

Let’s help collect the food that is left over.

Gosh!
Look how many baskets we’ve filled.

Isn't Jesus WONDERFUL!!

Time for a big hug.
What a wonderful day it's been!
I bet we'll have lots more adventures tomorrow.

Night, night everyone!

I love you, Jesus!

Premkala

Premkala is 12 years old – and very pretty. Guess what her name means? It means love-heart. She lives on a small farm in a country called Nepal.

One day, a few years ago, she became sick with a disease called leprosy. Her grandfather helped her walk for two days to find a doctor. Now she is much better and very happy!

But there are other children in her country who are sick and need help like Premkala. Let's say a prayer together for all children who feel poorly – wherever they are.

Dear Jesus

Thank you for all the people who work with you, helping girls and boys get well and strong.

Help me to be like you – and love everyone.

Amen